THE

ECLECTIC FIRST READER,

FOR

YOUNG CHILDREN.

CONSISTING OF

PROGRESSIVE LESSONS

IN

READING AND SPELLING

MOSTLY IN

EASY WORDS OF ONE AND TWO SYLLABLES

———◆●◆———

BY WILLIAM H. McGUFFEY,
Professor in Miami University, Oxford

———◆●◆———

— 1836 —

CINCINNATI:
PUBLISHED BY TRUMAN AND SMITH
150 MAIN STREET

ROMAN NUMERALS EXPLAINED.

A numeral is a symbol meaning number. Our system of counting is believed to have begun by people counting on their fingers. Both the Arabic (1, 2, 3, 4, etc.) and the Roman (I, II, III, IV, etc.) are believed to have started this way. The word digit, meaning number, is from the Latin word digitus, meaning finger. The number V (5) seems to be representative of an open hand; and, the number X (10) seems to be like two open hands.

In earlier days, our forefathers used the Roman system to indicate chapter headings in books. To help you understand those numbers more easily you may refer to the chart below:

Roman	Arabic	Roman	Arabic	Roman	Arabic
I	1	XI	11	XXX	30
II	2	XII	12	XL	40
III	3	XIII	13	L	50
IV	4	XIV	14	LX	60
V	5	XV	15	LXX	70
VI	6	XVI	16	LXXX	80
VII	7	XVII	17	XC	90
VIII	8	XVIII	18	C	100
IX	9	XIX	19	D	500
X	10	XX	20	M	1000

Entered according to Act of Congress, in the year 1836
By TRUMAN & SMITH,
In the Clerk's Office for the District Court of Ohio.

ISBN 0-88062-002-1
Printed in the United States of America

PRESENT PUBLISHER'S PREFACE.

Out-of-print for over 125 years, the *original* McGuffey's Eclectic Readers are considered educational classics. These books are world renowned for their teaching of reading through the integration of faith with learning.

William Holmes McGuffey, outstanding 19th century educator and preacher, combined both of his God-given talents in the preparation of these early textbooks. Millions of copies were sold in their *original* Christ-centered form. The character of our Nation was molded in an upright manner through the repeated use of these textbooks over several generations.

In order to capture the true spirit of the *original* McGuffey's Eclectic Readers we have made no major content changes. While this edition of the *authentic* Readers is being presented in a more easily readable form, the stories, poems, and pictures appear as they did in the first edition. Slight changes have taken place for the sake of clarification.

The Publisher wishes to express his heart-felt appreciation to the staff of the Special Collections Library at Miami University, Oxford, Ohio, for its cooperation in researching the *authenticity* of this book. Additionally, we desire to thank Dr. John H. Westerhoff, III, for his inspiration in promoting the republishing of the *original* works and Bohn Printing for their untiring efforts in typesetting the Readers.

It is indeed an honor and distinct pleasure to return the *original* McGuffey's Eclectic Readers to you. The content of this series will help you develop outstanding reading skills, Christ-centered character, a love for good literature, and impressive speaking abilities. I am sure you will find the *original* McGuffey's Eclectic Readers to be a valuable teaching tool whether they are used in the public school, Christian school, or for those who choose to teach their children at home.

George M. Mott, President
MOTT MEDIA, INC.

LESSON I.

The New Book.

Here is John.

There are Ann and Jane.

Ann has a new book.

It is the first book.

Ann must keep it nice and clean.

John must not tear the book.
He may see how fast he can
learn.

———————◆———————

John	and	there	learn
Ann	has	here	nice
Jane	must	keep	clean

LESSON II.

This boy has a bird.
This bird is on his hand.
Some birds can talk.

The dog barks.
Do you hear the dog bark?
Boys play with dogs.

The boys run fast.

They run as fast as they can.

One of the boys has no hat.

Here is a small dog.

He has the boy's hat.

The boys can not get it.

LESSON III.

This horse eats hay.

The hay is on the ground.

Hay is made of grass.

The two boys go to school.

The bags are for their books.

Do you go to school?

This cow is in the pond.

The cow gives us milk.

You must not hurt the cow.

The hen eats corn.

The hen picks up the corn.

Can the little chicks eat corn?

LESSON IV.

The Wild Ox.

An ox has two horns. He has four legs, and four feet.

A wild ox will toss boys on his horns.

The ox draws the plow and the cart. He is large and strong, and he works hard for man.

An ox has red, white, or black hair. He eats grass, hay, corn, and drinks water.

He lies down on his side when he sleeps.

———◆———

ox	has	two	horns
he	four	legs	feet
and	hard	man	hay

LESSON V.

The Cat and the Dog.

Do you see the cat and the dog? We call a cat, Puss.

Puss is up on the wall. The dog barks, but he can not catch her.

Puss has sharp claws, and sharp teeth.

If you pull her hair or tail, she will scratch or bite you. Give Puss some milk, then she will love you. Little boys and girls should not hurt the dog or the cat.

———

cat	milk	pull	hair
dog	love	teeth	give
Puss	you	barks	little
catch	claws	bite	sharp

LESSON VI.

The Boy and Dog.

See how this dog stands on his hind feet. He wants to play with John.

A dog has four feet. A dog and a cat can see in the dark.

The dog keeps watch at night, and barks.

Dogs bark most when the moon shines.

A dog will chase a sheep, hog, or cow, and bite it.

If you are kind to the dog, he will not bite you.

---

his	dark	sheep	watch
four	feet	chase	night
hind	keeps	shines	stands

LESSON VII.

The Bear.

Did you ever see a bear? A bear is like a large dog, with long brown hair, and a short tail.

The bear is very strong.

He lives in a den in the woods.

The bear can run up a tree, like Puss. He is very strong and likely to be cross. We call the bear Bruin.

LESSON VIII.

Time to Get Up.

Mama, may I get up?

Yes, my child, you may. The sun is up and the dew has gone from the grass.

It is cool now, but it will soon be hot. When the sun gets high in the sky, it will be warm.

I will go out on the porch and spin my top.

---

yes	when	now	up
out	warm	sun	porch
child	grass	hot	cool

LESSON IX.

The Poor Old Man.

Jane, there is a poor old man at the door.

He asks for something to eat. We will give him some bread and cheese.

He is cold. Will you give him some clothes too?

I will give him a suit of old clothes which will be new to him.

Poor man! I wish he had a warm house, and kind friends to live with him. He would not have to beg from door to door.

We should be kind to the poor. We may be as poor as this old man, and need as much as he.

Shall I give him some money to buy a pair of shoes?

No, you may give him a pair of shoes.

It is hard for the poor to have to beg from house to house.

Poor boys and girls sometimes have to sleep out of doors all night. When it snows they are very cold, and when it rains, they get quite wet.

Who is it that gives us food to eat, and clothes to make us warm?

It is God, my child; He makes the sun to shine, and sends the rain upon the earth, that we may have food.

God makes the little lambs bring forth wool, that we may have clothes to keep us warm.

———————

Jane	poor	some	eat
old	asks	thing	give
man	him	bread	cheese
cold	will	should	you
something		clothes	

LESSON X.

The Sun is Up.

See, the sun is up. The sun gives us light. It makes the trees and the grass grow.

The sun rises in the east and sets in the west. When the sun rises, it is day.

When the sun sets it is night.

This little boy was up at five. He saw the sun rise, and heard the sweet songs of birds on every bush.

Do you know who made the sun?

God made it.

God made the moon and all the stars. How good God is to us. He gives us all we have, and keeps us alive.

We should love God.

God sees and knows all

things, for God is everywhere. He sees me when I rise from my bed, and when I go out to walk and play. When I lie down to sleep at night, He keeps me from harm.

Though I do not see the wind, yet it blows around me on all sides. God is with me at all times, and yet I see Him not.

If God is with me, and knows all that I do, He must hear what I say. Oh, let me not, then, speak bad words. If I do, God will not love my ways.

---

sun	grass	should	must
light	then	makes	hear
birds	things	knows	east
little	boy	all	five
sweet	birds	every	bush
God	sees	when	rise
how	play	sides	sleep
hear	though	times	say
keeps	harm	speak	words

LESSON XI.

Boys at Play.

Can you fly a kite? See how the boy flies his kite. He holds the string tight, and the wind blows it up in the sky.

Now it is high in the air,

and looks like a bird. When the wind blows hard, you must hold fast, or your kite will get away.

Boys love to run and play.

They must not be rude. Good boys do not play in a rude way, but they take care not to hurt any one.

You must not lie. Bad boys lie, and swear, and steal.

When boys are at play they must be kind, and not feel cross. If you are cross, good boys will not like to play with you.

When you fall down, you must not cry, but get up, and run again. If you cry, the boys will call you a baby.

Some boys use bad words when they are at play. The Bible says that you must not use bad words. You must mind what the Bible says, for it is God's book. You must not play with boys that speak bad words or tell lies.

kite	holds	wind	high
string	fast	blows	looks
bird	when	boys	baby
words	play	you	not
speak	bad	book	but
Bible	hurt	rude	take
care	one	they	cry
get	up	run	again
kind	not	feel	cross
must	mind	good	says
boys	lie	swear	steal

LESSON XII.

Robert and his Horse.

Here is a fine horse.

Has the horse been fed?

Give him some hay and some oats.

The horse lives on grain; he does not eat meat.

Men eat meat, bears eat meat, and dogs eat meat. Horses, sheep, and cows do not eat meat.

May I ride on the horse? No, you are too small. When you grow to be as big as John, you may ride.

---

fed	fine	been	grain
hay	oats	give	small
too	ride	meat	sheep

LESSON XIII.

The Walk.

Come, Mary, get your bonnet, and we will take a walk.

See, the sun is in the west. It is going to set. How large it looks. We may look at it now. It is not so bright now, as when it was up high in the sky. It will soon be out of sight. Now it is almost gone.

How red the clouds are. We can see the moon, and all the

pretty stars, when the sun sets. The moon is not so bright as the sun.

See the pretty bright stars. Some of the stars are as large as the world. But they are so far away, that they look small.

Papa, is the sun as large as the world?

Yes, my son, and a great deal larger, but it is far away.

hat	high	away	Mary
walk	sky	small	pretty
take	now	make	larger
come	gone	sight	bonnet
get	red	papa	going

LESSON XIV.

The Lame Man.

See that poor man. He is lame and has no hat on his head.

John, will you give him your old hat? Yes, you will. You will be glad to help him.

We must feel for the lame, and do all we can to help them. John, you are a kind boy, and I love you.

Poor old man! He is sad— he is in want. Ah, see how pale he is! He is sick. Come in poor man, come in. We will give you a bit of cake to eat, and some milk. John will give you a hat.

Look now at that sick boy. He is not sick for want of food. He had a cake sent to him and he was told not to eat too much of it, yet he did.

The cake has made him sick. See how his face is pale and sad. If he had not done that, he would not be ill.

Now he is so sick he can scarcely go out this fine day. He can not run, nor jump, nor play. I hope you will not act like this boy. Mind what is said. Do not eat more than is good for you, so that you will not look pale like him or feel sick as he does.

that	poor	man	lame
must	feel	help	them
will	give	him	your
told	none	sent	done
come	cake	some	milk
much	that	made	face
hope	mind	what	said
more	than	jump	may
pale	good	been	does

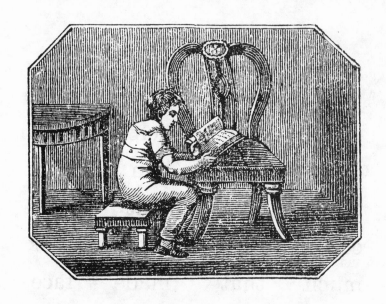

LESSON XV.

Little Henry.

Well, Henry, what have you read in your new book?

I read of three boys who went to school.

Each of them had a fine large cake. James ate so

much that it made him sick.
George kept his so long that
it got dry, and was not fit to
eat.

John gave some of his cake
to each of his school mates,
and then took a piece himself.
He gave the rest to an old
blind man.

The old man could not see
to work for his food. So John
gave him a share of his cake.

How kind John was! I love
kind boys and girls.

We must be kind and good
to the blind.

If we were blind, we would be glad to meet with kind folks, who would give us something to eat.

When I have read my book, Ann, I will lend it to you, and I will read to Jane. I dare say it is a nice one. I am sure you will take care of it.

Aunt says, that no one but a bad girl will tear or soil a book. How glad I am to have a kind aunt and a good book.

Henry	James	George	Ann
book	poor	got	thing
dry	blind	made	have
long	more	then	that
large	glad	kept	much
took	good	girls	fine
some	rest	was	went
mates	piece	boys	see
aunt	says	none	soil

LESSON XVI.

The Good Girl.

Mama, may I sew today?

Yes my child. What do you wish to sew?

I wish to hem a frill for your cap. Is not this a new cap? I see it has no frill.

You may make the frill for me. I shall like to wear a frill that you have made. Here is a bit of cloth which will make a nice frill. You must hem it. I will turn it down for you, but take care not to soil it.

Wash your hands, and take care to wipe them dry. Now sit down on your low stool. Now you may go on. You will see best here by my side.

You must join these two pieces with a seam. When you have sewn as far as this pin, bring it to me to see.

Jane sat down upon her stool and sewed like a little lady. In a short time she said, Mama, I have sewn as far as you told me. Will you look at it?

Yes, my child, it is well done. If you take pains, as you have done today, you will soon sew well.

I wish to sew well, Mama. Then I can help you to make caps, and frocks, and I hope to be of some help to you.

pray	cloth	wipe	these
sew	hands	dry	look
hem	frill	pains	you
new	clean	stood	hope
bits	were	seam	told
frocks	bring	shirts	soil
caps	child	side	low
sat	down	upon	served
like	little	lady	short
time	wish	hope	care

help

LESSON XVII.

About James Smith.

Ann Smith had but one child, and his name was James. Ann was poor, but she did her best to work hard, that she might pay for her house, and buy food and clothes.

Her house was small and stood near the road. There were two small rooms in it— one in which to sleep, and one in which to live. She made a bed in the room where she had to live. James slept in this bed.

In this room she had one chair, one low stool for James to sit on, a few cups and plates, and some other things that she had bought. In the room where she slept, she had her own bed, and a box made of wood, in which she kept her clothes.

James was so fond of her, that he would run out to meet her, when she came home at night from her work. When she left him to go to work, he

would sit on a large stone
near the door of the house.
He would look at her as long
as he could see her, and then
he would cry, and wish for
her to come back to him.

James went to school. He
studied so much that in a few
months he could read. Poor
Ann Smith was glad of this.
When she came home from
work, James would read to
her from a large book which
a kind friend had given him.

Some day I will tell you
what was in that book, and I

think you will love to hear it, and to read it, as James Smith did.

———

food	room	child	Smith
gone	come	night	things
went	meet	slept	would
hate	back	large	friend
Ann	much	board	school
poor	work	pains	clothes
care	made	ready	bought
had	stool	small	weight
own	home	stood	James
door	fond	crate	might
then	wood	warm	house
him	look	large	months
hail	kind	plates	ground

LESSON XVIII.

The Thick Shade.

Come, let us go into thick shade. It is noonday, and the summer sun beats hot upon our heads.

The shade is pleasant and

cool. The branches meet above our heads and shut out the sun like a green curtain.

The grass is soft to our feet, and the clear brook washes the roots of the trees.

The cattle can lie down to sleep in the cool shade, but we can do better. We can raise our voices to heaven. We can praise the great God who made us.

He made the warm sun and the cool shade, the trees that grow upwards, and the brooks that run along.

The plants and trees are made to give fruit to man.

All that live get life from God. He made the poor man, as well as the rich man.

He made the dark man, as well as the fair man. He made the fool, as well as the wise man. All that move on the land are His, and so all that fly in the air, and all that swim in the sea.

The ox and the worm are both the work of His hand. In Him, they live and move. He it is that doth give food to all

of them, and when He says
the word, they all must die.

———————

come	clear	sleep
shade	down	heaven
heads	voices	thick
soft	pleasant	heat
cattle	into	branches
raise	day	upwards
noon	cool	better
trees	brook	summer

LESSON XIX.

The Lame Dog.

One day a man went to take a walk in the town. On his way home, he saw a little dog which had hurt his leg. The poor dog was so lame he could not lift his foot off the ground without great pain.

When this kind man saw there was no one to take pity on the poor dog, he took him in his arms, and brought him home and bound up his leg. Then he fed him and made a warm place, and kept him in his house for two days.

He then sent the dog out of his house, to his old home. Since it was not his own dog, he had no right to keep him, but each day the dog came back for this kind man to dress his leg. This he did till he was quite well.

In a few weeks, the dog came back once more, and with him came a dog that was lame.

The dog that had been lame and was now well, first gave the man a look, and then he gave the lame dog a look, as much as to say:

"You made my lame leg well, and now pray do the same for this poor dog that has come with me."

day	poor	there
town	could	same
right	pain	and
quite	kind	take
great	found	saw
off	house	gone
been	went	lame
has	home	foot
good	dog	feet
man	for	arms
once	his	then
little	ground	kept

LESSON XX.

John Jones.

John Jones was a good boy, but he could not read nor write. His mother was poor. She could not pay for him to go to school. She sent him out to help a man at the side of the road to break stones. John could not earn much, it is true, yet it was good for him to be at work.

It is well for us all to have work to do. It is bad for us not to work. John was a good boy, and he did not love to play so much that he could not work. He knew it to be right to work, and when his work was done he would play.

The man for whom John worked was very kind to John, and gave him a great deal of good advice.

One day he said to him, "John, you must always bear in mind, that it was God who made you, and who gave you all that you have, and all that you hope for. He gave you life, and food, and a home.

"All who take care of you and help you were sent you by God. He sent His Son to show you His will, and to die for your sake.

"He gave you His word to let you know what He hath done for you, and what He wants you to do.

"Be sure that He sees you in the dark, as well as in the day light. He can tell all that you do, and all that you say, and all that is in your mind.

"Oh, ever seek this God! Pray to Him when you rise,

and when you lie down. Keep His day, hear His word, and do His will, and He will love you, and will be your God for ever."

---

have	live	know
pray	good	him
done	advice	down
food	always	hath
your	some	help
worked	sees	read
very	hope	mind
kind	word	ever

great	sent	dark
gave	that	light
you	whom	seek
die	show	deal
life	day	bear

LESSON XXI.

About The Moon.

The moon is very large.

See how red it is!

It looks like blood!

The moon is round now, because it is full moon.

It will not be so round the next night. The moon will lose a little, and the next night a little more, and so on until it is like your bow when it is bent. It will not be seen until after you are in bed. It will grow less and less, until in two weeks there will be no moon at all.

After that, there will be a new moon. You will see it just before night, and it will be very thin at first.

It will grow round and larger each day, until at last, in two weeks more, it will be a full moon again like this. You will see it rise again behind the trees, in four weeks from this time, just as you see it now.

If we had no moon, it would be very dark at night. We

could not see to walk, or do anything.

When there is snow on the ground, and the moon shines, it is almost as bright as day. When there is no moon, and the stars do not shine, it is very dark.

———————

moon	more	first
red	bow	again
large	like	because
very	weeks	behind
blood	new	almost
lose	before	every
little	thin	snow

LESSON XXII.

The School Girl.

Jane Rice is a good girl. She goes to school every day, and she can read quite well. She does what she is told, and is kind to all.

One day, as she went to school, she saw a poor bee in the water, on the road. She took a leaf, for fear the bee would sting her, and held it to the bee.

The bee took hold of it, with its feet. Jane took it out,

and put it where the sun
would shine on it. The bee
soon got warm and flew
away. Jane was glad that she
had saved its life.

---

leaf	quite	water
fear	shine	school
warm	away	would
glad	saved	where

LESSON XXIII.

The Kind Boy.

James Bland found a poor young bird on the cold ground. It was all wet, for there had been rain that day. "Ha!" said he, "I will have a fine pet, now." James took it home. He met his sister Ann at the door.

"Here, Ann," said he, "is a young bluebird. I found it in the road. We will put it in a cage and keep it." Ann looked at it. "Poor thing," said she, "it is cold. Let us take it to the fire."

She took it, and warmed it. As soon as it was dry and warm, it began to chirp and tried to get away.

Ann told James that it would be cruel to keep the

bird. "See, it wants to go back to its nest. We would not like to be taken from home and kept in a cage."

James thought so too, so he took the bird to the door. "There! Go, poor bird," said he, and away it flew.

Some boys would have kept it, and maybe it would have died. But James was a good boy, and would not be cruel, even to a bird.

I hope that no boy who reads this book will ever rob

a bird's nest. It is very cruel
and wicked.

———————

cold	the	boy
wet	sister	who
way	kept	wicked
cage	good	warm
cruel	that	nest
looked	ever	rain
began	back	poor
taken	ground	flew
bluebird	dry	door
have	thing	reads
shall	bird	very
	blue	though

LESSON XXIV.

The New Slate.

Here is a little boy who had a new slate given him. It was bought for him by his father, that he might learn arithmetic. One day he made some pictures on his slate.

Look here, Charles, I have drawn a boy on my new slate. See what a long nose he has! Ah! He has but one arm.

Now I will draw a milk maid with her pail.

There, I have drawn a pig, and a hen, and a duck. Why the pig has but two legs, and the duck has four. Well, I can rub out two of the duck's legs and give them to the pig.

There, now I will draw a man with a whip in his hand. The man has come to put the pig in the pen.

Why, the man is not as tall as the pig. I must rub them all out, for they are not well done.

There, I have a boy with a nest full of eggs in his hand. He is a bad boy to take a poor bird's nest.

And here is Betty, the maid. She has come to take me to bed. Well if it is time, I must go. Put my slate away, that I may have it safe when I want to draw.

Charles	them	hand
Betty	done	put
drawn	nest	long
little	may	maid
given	what	must
father	will	draw
pictures	pail	man
new	four	eggs
now	all	bad
with	want	have
	duck	

LESSON XXV.

What the Animals Say.

The fly says, I fly in the air, if the sun is hot. I sip out of the tea cups. If I see a boy at tea, I sit on the rim of the cup and sip his tea. If he sees me, he may try to pat me, if he can. I fly away and up in the air, so he can not get me. I am a swift fly.

The bee says, I fly too, if the sun is hot, and if it is not wet. I sip too, but I do not get in the tea cups. I am helpful. Boys do not try to pat me, for I do not get in the way, and boys can see I am helpful. If they catch me and do anything to hurt me, I will sting them.

The cat says, I do not sip, I lap. I can get a rat, and I can get you, Mr. Fly, if you do not go too far up the the air. I can run, mew, and can lie in the sun. If it is not hot, I lie on the rug, or in my bed of hay.

The rat says, I eat all I can get. The cat may try to get me, if she can, but I can run out of her way.

The hen says, I can fly, but not as far as Tom, the small bird. I lay eggs, and I am useful to man, but the fox may get me, and so may the rats.

The fox says, I am sly, and try to eat all the old hens, but

the dogs and men hear me,
and try to get me. I am so sly,
it is odd if the dogs and men
can get me at all.

———————◆———————

fly	see	and
says	eggs	but
cup	wet	sun
can	try	tea
get	air	pat
boys	sip	bee
the	off	use
hot	air	was

LESSON XXVI.

The Cruel Boy.

George Craft is a very cruel boy. He is only six years old, and yet he is very bad.

George would catch flies, and pull off their wings and legs, and then laugh to see them hop. The dog and cat are both afraid of George, and will run and hide when they see him. One day, last week, a young friend of his came to see him, and was very angry at his conduct.

He asked George how he would like to have his legs and arms pulled off. George hung his head. Why, said he, flies cannot feel much. His friend told him, that he had heard men say that everything that could move, could feel, and that it was wrong of anyone to hurt or kill them.

George felt very sorry, when he heard his young friend tell him how bad he had acted, and I hope he will not do so any more.

———————◆———————

George	cruel	hide
asked	pulled	young
everything	conduct	heard
came	laugh	legs
wrong	angry	wings
friend	week	catch

LESSON XXVII.

How to Add.

John. I wish I could do a sum, as James does. May I get a slate and try?

Mother. You can not use a slate yet, but I will teach you how to add with these beans. Now, mind what I say to you. Here is one, and here are two more. How many do one and two beans make?

Put them in your left hand, and count one, two, three.

You see that one and two make three.

Now take three more beans, and add them to those in your left hand, and count all of them—one, two, three, four, five, six. Three and three make six.

Now take four beans, and add two more to them. You see there are six. Four and two are six. Now take five beans, and add one to them. You see there are six. Then five and one make six.

could	beans	four
these	hand	teach
your	slate	here
does	mind	three

LESSON XXVIII.

The Wild Beasts.

James and George went to the show. They saw a great many wild beasts in cages, and some only with a chain around one foot, fastened to a post.

They saw the showman go into a cage with the lion and strike him with a cow hide. The lion roared very loud, and looked cross, but did not hurt him.

James said, "I wish the

man would come out. I do not like to see him in the cage. That big lion might eat him and then I should be sorry." James was a good boy, and did not like to see anyone hurt.

After they had seen the show their kind papa took them to the book store, and bought each of them a fine new book.

They were good boys, and loved to read.

seen   many   book

kind   roared   papa

bought   looked   loved

show   cow   before

good   hide   beasts

quite   cross   James

through   store

LESSON XXIX.

The Story Teller.

Peter Parley was a great story teller. This is known to all children who have read his books. One day as he was going by the school, the children came around him, and they all wished him to tell them a new story.

"Well," says Peter, "I love to please good children, and as you all appear kind and civil, I will tell you a story which you have never heard. Before we begin, let us go and sit down in a cool shady place.

"And now, master John, you must be as still as a little mouse. And Mary, you must be careful not to let Towser bark and make a noise.

"A long way from this place, in a land where it is very cold, and where much snow falls, and where the hills are so high that their tops appear to reach the sky, there live some men whose joy it is to help folks who pass by these hills.

"These men keep large dogs, which they teach to go out and hunt for persons who may be lost in the snow drifts. The dogs have so fine a scent or smell, that they can find folks by means of it.

Even when it is too dark to see, or when the folks for whom they are searching, lie hidden in the deep snow drifts, they find them."

———————•———————

whose	begin	scent
much	high	deep
great	drift	Parley
please	hid	Towser
appear	story	Mary
persons	books	master
children	going	wished
teller	down	never
have	these	careful
	read	

LESSON XXX.

The Snow Dog and Boy.

After the old man had wiped the sweat from off his face, he went on with his story.

"One sad, cold night when the snow fell fast, and the

wind blew loud and shrill, and it was quite dark with not a star to be seen in the sky, these good men sent out a dog to hunt for those who might want help.

"In an hour or two the dog was heard at the gate, and when they looked they saw the dog with a boy on his back.

"The poor child was stiff with cold, and could just hold on to the dog's back.

"He told the men that he had lain a long time in the

snow, and was too ill and weak to walk, and the snow fell fast on him. After a while, he felt something pull him by the coat, and then he heard the bark of a dog close by him.

"The boy then put out his hand, and he felt the hair of the dog, and then the dog gave him one more pull. This gave the poor boy some hope, and he took hold of the dog, and drew himself out of the snow. He felt that he could not stand or walk.

"He then got upon the dog's back, and put his arms around the dog's neck, and held fast. He felt sure the dog did not mean to hurt him, and thus he rode on the dog's back, all the way to the good men's house. They took care of the boy till the snow was gone, then they sent him to his own home."

———————◆·◆———————

sweat	wiped	mean
might	something	home
snow	heard	could
after	length	quite

LESSON XXXI.

Good Advice.

If you have done anything during the day that is wrong, ask forgiveness of God and your parents.

Remember that you should learn some good things every day. If you have learned nothing all day, that day is lost.

If anyone has done you wrong, forgive him in your

heart before you go to sleep. Do not go to sleep with hatred in your heart toward anyone.

Never speak to anyone in an angry or harsh voice.

If you have spoken unkind words to a brother or sister, go and ask forgiveness.

If you have disobeyed your parents, go and confess it.

Ask God to aid you always to do good and avoid evil.

before   parents   during

always   brother   forgive

shaken   unkind   forgiveness

hatred   confess   remember

nothing   sister   disobeyed

LESSON XXXII.

Little Lucy.

Lucy, can you read?

Yes sir, I can. Would you rather read than play? Yes sir, I would, because mama tells me that play will not be of any use to me after I am grown. If I love to read, I will be wise and good.

A little boy or girl who can not read is not much better than Puss. Puss can run and play, as well as they. Puss can never learn to read. Boys who do not know how to read can not learn anything, but what is told to them.

When a boy or girl knows how to read, they can sit down and learn a great deal, when there is no one to talk to them.

After boys and girls have learned to read, they can learn to write. Then they can send letters to their friends, who live far away.

know   can not   because

friends   mama   away

much   rather   letters

learned   better   never

LESSON XXXIII.

Peter Holt.

One day Peter Holt was left at home by his parents, while they went out to take a ride.

His mama told him to stay in the house until she came back. "Be very sure that you do not go out among the horses," said she. "They may hurt you."

Peter said he would do as he was told. So his mama kissed him, and she left.

He soon was very tired of staying in the house. Soon he ran down to the lot to look at a little colt which his papa had given him.

It was very tame, so he put his hand on its neck, and then on its head. At last he thought it was so tame and gentle that he would ride it. He led it to the fence, and jumped on its back. The colt had never before felt anything on his back, and was very much alarmed. It put down its head, and ran away at a great rate, and at last, kicked up its hind feet, and threw Peter over its head.

Peter was hurt very much, but he crept home, as well as he could. If he had been so badly hurt as not to be able to get home, he might have died in the field before his mama came home.

Little children may learn from this, that they should always obey their parents. How many little girls and boys have been hurt because they did not do as they were told!

———————◆◆◆———————

thing	crept	kicked
down	hunt	before
good	much	gentle
should	that	children
went	when	staying
came	they	kissed
field	were	many
house	Peter	parents
home	little	jumped
tame	obey	always
learn	given	because
their	never	alarmed

then   badly   carriage
ream   over   directly
            back

LESSON XXXIV.

About Mr. Post.

Mr. Post lives in a small house in New York. He is quite an old man, and yet he has no one to live with him. He cooks his own food, for he is poor, and can not hire anyone to do it for him.

When he was young, he went to the wars, and had his leg shot off. But he had a leg made of wood, and can walk very well on it. He loves boys and girls. Whenever they come to see him, he often tells them how he was shot.

He takes his staff for a gun, and shows the little boys how to use it.

The little girls are very fond of Mr. Post, for they love to hear him talk.

Sometimes they bring him milk, which pleases him very much.

New York	pleases	very
Mr. Post	sometimes	quite
cooks	young	wood
loves	small	takes
any	staff	which
alone	much	talk
	little	

LESSON XXXV.

Mr. Post and the Little Girls.

One cold night, after old Mr. Post had gone to bed, he heard a noise at the door. He got up, and went outside.

What do you think he found? A dog? No. A goat?

No. He found a little babe on the steps.

Some bad person had left it there. If Mr. Post had not taken it into the house, it might have died with cold. He held it near the fire, until it was warm, and then took it in his arms, and went to bed.

Old Mr. Post was kind. He did not know what to do with the innocent little babe, but he could not let it die.

When Mr. Post's little friends came to see him the next day, they thought it

very strange to see him have
a little babe with him. He told
them how he got the babe,
and they all said that they
would bring it milk, and
sometimes come and help
him to take care of it.

The little girl was named
Mary. Soon she was very
fond of Mr. Post, and called
him papa. In a short time,
she grew so large that she
could run and open the gate
for her papa, when he was going out.

Mr. Post taught her to

read, and at night Mary would read the Bible to her papa.

Mary was soon able to get the dinner, and do little chores, and when her papa got so old that he could not work, Mary took care of him.

Mary	dinner	into
going	open	sometimes
died	called	innocent
until	papa	person

LESSON XXXVI.

Kids are Little Goats.

Goats do not like to live in the streets and houses like dogs and pigs. Goats love to run and jump about in the fields, and to eat the bark of trees. Goats give very thick rich milk.

People can not carry cows to sea in ships, so they take goats. Goats are much smaller than cows, and do not take so much room in the ships. Without goats, the men in the ships would not have milk for their tea.

Once there was a little girl who lived in a place where there were a great many goats. One day she took a walk and found a little kid. The old goat, the mother of the little kid, had left it, and it was almost dead.

Mary felt sorry for the poor little thing. She took it up in her arms, and carried it home with her. Her mother let her keep the kid for her own.

Mary got some clean straw and laid it on the warm hearth to make a bed for the kid. She warmed some milk and held it to him to drink.

The kid drank it, and lick-ed Mary's hand for more. Mary was very much pleased when she saw him jump out of the straw, and run about the room.

By and by, he lay down again, and took a fine nap. The next day Mary named her kid Tom. Tom soon learn-ed to follow Mary about the house, and trot by her side into the yard. He would run races with her in the field, feed out of her hand, and was a great pet at all times.

One fine warm day, after Mary had done her morning work, she went out to play with her kid. She looked about the house door and could not see Tom. She then ran to the field, and called, "Tom! Tom!"

Tom had found a flock of goats, and was playing with them. He loved to stay with

them, better than with Mary.
Mary went home crying, and
it was a long time before she
forgot her little Tom.

---

streets   mother   forget

place   warmed   follow

straw   smaller   crying

goats   without   morning

houses   pleased   carried

         people

LESSON XXXVII.

Evening Prayer.

At the close of the day, before you go to sleep, you should not fail to pray to God to keep you from sin and from harm.

You ask your parents for food, and drink, and books, and clothes, and when they give you these things, you thank them, and love them for the good they do you.

So you should ask your God for those things which He can give you, and which no one else can give you.

You should ask Him for life, and health and strength. You should pray to Him to keep your feet from the ways of sin and shame.

You should thank Him for

all His good gifts, and learn, while young, to put your trust in Him. The kind care of God will be with you, both in your youth and in your old age.

———————◆———————

close	food	those
fail	these	young
friends	should	would
clothes	learn	harm
good	sleep	books
strength	from	them
before	drink	which
pray	things	youth

LESSON XXXVIII.

The Boy who told a Lie.

There was once a boy whose father sent him to ride a few miles on an errand. He told him not to stop by the way. It was a fine sunny morning, and he rode by the green trees, and heard the sweet songs of the birds. He seemed to feel as happy as they.

After he had done his errand, he started to come

home. As he was riding by a house where two of his playmates lived, he thought he would stop a few moments to see them. The boy stayed longer, and longer, until two hours had been spent playing.

With a heavy heart, he now mounted his horse again. He rode slowly along, thinking what excuse he should make to his father for not coming home sooner.

The boy trembled and turned pale, as he saw his

father. When his kind father came up to him, he said, "Father, I lost the road, and it took me some time to get back again, and that is the reason why I have been gone so long."

His father had never known him to be guilty of such an act before, and believed what his son told him. Oh, how guilty and ashamed did that boy feel, as he walked along by his father. His look of innocence was gone, and he was ashamed to look his father or his mother in the face. He tried to appear easy and happy, but he was uneasy and miserable.

———————

errand	moments	trembled
sunny	mounted	morning
riding	ashamed	playmates
uneasy	reason	miserable

LESSON XXXIX.

*More about the Little Boy
who told a Lie.*

When the little boy, whom
you last read about, went to
bed that night, he was afraid.
He knew that he had done
wrong, and it was long before
he could quiet his troubled
spirit with sleep.

Thus, things went on for
two or three weeks. One day
a man made a business call to
see the father of this boy. As

soon as the boy saw him come into the house, his heart beat quickly, and he turned pale. He feared that something would be said that would bring the whole truth to light.

After talking a few moments with his father, the man turned to the little boy, and said, "Well, how did you get home the other day? My boys had a very pleasant visit from you."

Can you think how this boy felt? You could have almost

heard his heart beat. The blood rushed into his face, and he could not speak, and he dared not raise his eyes from the floor.

The man then turned to his father, and said, "You must let your son come up again, and see my boys. When he was there about two weeks ago, he only stayed about two hours, and they hoped he had come to spend the whole day with them."

Now the whole truth was out. The boy stood before his

parents covered with shame. How bitterly had he suffered. The guilty boy burst into tears, and implored his parents' forgiveness.

But he was told by his parents that he had sinned, not only against them, but against God. The humble child went to God in penitence and in prayer. He made a full confession of all to his parents, and obtained their forgiveness, and it was not till then that peace of mind was restored.

when   truth   parents

whom   must   stayed

weeks   come   penitence

soon   spend   sufferer

said   whole   covered

could   almost   obtained

floor   guilty   business

raise   dawned   implored

shame   pleasant   confession

them   turned   forgiveness

peace   sinned

LESSON XL.

The Little Chimney Sweep.

Some time ago, there was a little chimney sweep, who had to sweep a chimney in the house of a very rich lady. The little sweep went up at the kitchen fire place, and came down in the chamber.

When he got into the chamber, he found himself all alone. He stopped a moment to look around at the rich furniture. As he looked on the top of the table, he saw an elegant gold watch, with gold seals to it.

He had never seen any-thing so beautiful before, and he took it in his hands. As he listened to hear it tick, it began to play sweet music. He then thought, if it only belonged to him, how rich he would be. He thought he might hide it in his blanket.

"Now," said he, "if I take it, I shall be a thief—and yet, no one sees me. No one! Does not God see me? Could I ever

again be good? Could I then
ever say my prayers again to
God? And what should I do
when I come to die?"

———————

chimney   elegant   prayers
sweep   thought   furniture
kitchen   blanket   beautiful
chamber   belonged   listened

LESSON XLI.

More about the Little Chimney Sweep.

While the little sweep boy was thinking about taking the lady's gold watch, he felt cold all over, and trembled with fear.

"No," said he, "I can not take this watch. I would rather be a sweep and always be poor, than steal." He laid the watch down, and crept up the chimney.

The lady who owned the watch was just in the next room, and she could look through and see, and hear all that passed. She did not say anything to the boy then, but let him go away.

The next day she sent for him, and when he came, she said to him, "Well, my little friend, why did you not take my watch yesterday?" The little sweep then fell upon his knees and told the lady all about it.

Since the little sweep did

not steal the gold watch, nor
tell any stories about it, the
lady let him stay and live in
her house. For many years,
she gave him good instruc-
tion. When he grew up, he
was a good pious man, and
always tried to remember the
commandment which says,
"Thou shalt not steal!"

Here we see the truth of the
old saying, "Honesty is the
best policy." Had this sweep
taken the lady's watch, he
would have stolen. Then he
would have been sent to jail.

He would also have sinned against God, and perhaps, never have become pious.

Let no little boy or girl ever take things without permission, for it is stealing, and they who steal are thieves.

Some children seem to think that to take an apple, or an orange, or some small thing, without permission, is no sin. They are mistaken.

You can not steal the smallest pin without it being a sin, nor without being seen by that eye which never sleeps.

It is by stealing small things that children become robbers, and have to be put in prison.

———————◆———————

become smallest   permission
robbers yesterday instructed
stories   remember
commandment

LESSON XLII.

Don't take Strong Drink.

No little boy or girl should ever drink rum or whisky, unless they want to become drunkards.

Men who drink strong drink are glad to have any excuse for doing it. One will drink it because he is so hot, and another will drink it because he is cold.

One will drink it when he is wet, and another because he

is dry—one will drink it because he is in company, and another, because he is alone, and another will put it into his glass of water to kill the insects!

Thus, the pure water from the brook is poisoned with the "drunkard's drink," and the man who uses it becomes a sot. Then he is seen tottering through the streets, a shame to himself and to all his family.

Oh, how dreadful to die a drunkard. The Bible says

that no drunkard shall inherit the Kingdom of Heaven.

Whisky makes the happy miserable, and it causes the rich to become poor.

On the next page we will tell you a story about the "Whisky Boy."

---

excuse   company   drunkards
sot   dreadful   tottering
        insects   poisoned

LESSON XLIII.

The Whiskey Boy.

Oh, that there were no such thing as whiskey; but there is, and there are some boys who even love it. I am now about to tell you of one who loved it so much that he would get tipsy every day. His name was John.

When John first tasted of whiskey, he did not love it. No, he did not want to see it again. But John's father mixed some whiskey with water, and put in some sugar. Then John liked it very well.

In a short time, John got so he could drink without the sugar, and then without any water. His friends told him he would be a drunkard if he did not stop.

John would not stop. He said that if his father could drink whiskey, he could.

Before John was eight years old, he was a dreadful object, and none of the boys would play with him.

His eyes were red, and his

face was red, and full of blisters. He was found drunk one day in the street, and carried to the poor house, where he died in two weeks. How do you think his father felt after teaching him to drink whiskey?

———————

would	dreadful	blisters
poor	before	tasted
again	object	father
drunkard	learning	carried

LESSON XLIV.

Never do Mischief.

A very fine looking little boy, named Henry, lived near one of our large public schools. There were other boys living in the same house with Henry.

One night, two of the boys planned together to frighten Henry. One of them hid himself under Henry's bed. About midnight, a loud rap was heard at the door, and in stalked the other boy.

He was frightfully dressed in a white sheet, and had a lighted candle in his hand. Just as he came in, the boy under the bed raised his back, and heaved up the bed in which Henry was lying.

Now mark what took place. Henry did not rise as early as usual that morning, and when some of the family went to call him, he would only answer by strange noises and cries! His reason was gone— he was deranged.

In the course of the first

year after this, his reason seemed to come to him again. Thus, what took place was partly made known. Some other things were found out by one of the boys.

Henry's reason soon left him again, and now he is a perfect idiot. True, he is not violent, and never engages in tearing and throwing things about the room.

He is harmless and gentle, and has been for many years. In the night, at about the time when the boys frightened him, he will cry out with horror, "Oh, they are coming! They are coming!"

———————

throwing   stalked   violent

midnight   seemed   deranged

tearing   lighted   frightened

planned   dressed   engaged

harmless   horror   frightfully

LESSON XLV.

The Nest of Young Birds.

Winter is now gone and the warm season is come. See! What does that boy have in his hand? It is a nest of young birds.

I wonder what he is going to do with them. I hope he will not kill them. Poor little birds! What a wicked boy, to take them from their parents!

I dare say he will be careful of them, and put them into a

cage and feed them, but he can not take as good care of them, nor feed them as well as the old birds.

Besides, it seems so cruel to shut them up in a cage, and not let them fly about in the air as other birds do!

Now he has put the nest on the ground, and has gone to his work and left them. The old birds can now come and feed them. Oh! I am so happy. I wish they could carry them back, but they can not.

would   careful   about

young   can not   happy

warm   going   carry

reason   parents   little

GOOD BYE.

Now, my little readers, we have come to the end of the book, and I must bid you good bye. Before we part, let me give you a little advice.

You are now a little child. You are but a few years old, and have not much wisdom. Therefore, always listen to your teacher and to your parents. They are older than you, and they know best what is for your good.

Little children, you must

love your parents. You should be kind to your teachers, and gentle to your brothers and sisters, and playfellows. Use no hard words. Be guilty of no ill-natured tricks, and tell no ill-natured tales.

Always do to other children as you wish them to do unto you. This is the "Golden Rule"—remember it in your play. Act upon it now, and when you are grown up, do not forget it.

If you have been a good child and learned your lessons well, you may now have the "Second Reader."